ALVIN GOES WILD

by Ross Bagdasarian and Janice Karman

illustrated by Corny Cole
color by Dennis Durrell

Random House 🏠 New York

Dave Seville and the Chipmunks were having a picnic in the country. Alvin had threatened to go on strike if the hardworking singing stars didn't get some time off.

"If one more fan chases me down the street," said Alvin, "or pops out of a trash can..."

"That's the price of fame," said Dave.

"Let's start the picnic!" Theodore said. "What's for lunch?"

Dave opened the picnic basket and handed sandwiches around.

"Oh, no!" cried Simon. "Look what's headed this way!"

A huge tour bus full of eager fans stopped right next to their table. The fans surrounded Alvin.

Alvin started to scribble a note to Dave. Just then a hand grabbed Alvin's sandwich right off his plate.

Alvin handed the note to Dave. It said: "That does it. I'm not talking until I get a *real* vacation. Signed, Alvin." In a flash Alvin was on his feet, chasing after the thief.

Moments later Alvin was high in a tree—face to face with a wild chipmunk who looked just like him.

"Gee...this is neat up here," said Alvin. "Is this where you live?"

The wild chipmunk nodded. Then he started gobbling Alvin's sandwich in case Alvin meant to grab it back.

"How would you like all the food you can eat?" asked Alvin.

Alvin's double nodded again.

"Great," said Alvin. "Just trade clothes with me and go home with Dave and my brothers."

So the wild chipmunk went back to the picnic area dressed like Alvin.

Alvin admired himself in his new Tarzan suit. Then, realizing he'd still had no lunch, he went off to find some.

He picked some berries off a bush. "Ugh," he said, spitting them out. He tried chewing on an acorn. "Ouch!" he cried. "You could break a tooth this way." He wandered farther and farther into the woods, poking among the plants and roots, when...

Whoosh! A rope grabbed Alvin's foot and swung him high in the air. He was trapped!

"HEL-L-L-P!" Alvin screamed.

A large bearded trapper called Grizzly Sam sprang up out of the bushes.

"What puny varmint is this?" he said.

"I'm Alvin—of Alvin and the Chipmunks. Get me down!"

"Sure, and I'm Johnny Cash," said Grizzly Sam.

"Call Dave Seville," said Alvin. "He'll tell you I'm famous."

"A famous varmint," mused the trapper. "Hmm. I could make some money on your return. And I think I've got a cage just your size."

Back home with Dave and Alvin's brothers, the wild chipmunk was looking for a good place to rest. Spying a potted palm, he jumped in and started to dig.

"Alvin! Quit that! Look at the mess you're making," said Dave. He got out the vacuum cleaner to sweep up the dirt.

WHIRRR! The motor roared into action.

The wild chipmunk's eyes almost popped out of his head. What was that awful noise? He leaped up onto the chandelier.

"Alvin! Get down from there!" said Dave.

Just then the telephone rang.

The ringing startled the wild chipmunk. He fell from the chandelier onto Dave's head just as Dave picked up the phone.

"Urrghh," said Dave.

"David Seville? This here's Grizzly Sam. Got a critter here named Alvin who says he's yours. For a small sum you can have him back agin."

"What kind of prank is this?" Dave yelled. "All my boys are home." He slammed down the phone.

"Imagine that Grizzly Sam guy telling me he had you, Alvin," said Dave. "Now get off my head and go get ready for dinner. We're going to your favorite restaurant."

Soon Dave and the chipmunks were sitting in the restaurant.

Theodore leaned toward the wild chipmunk and whispered, "Alvin, do you use the little fork or the big fork for the appetizer?"

Alvin's double just grabbed a handful of the appetizer and shoved it into his mouth. Theodore shrugged and then did the same.

"Dave," said Simon, "Alvin's been acting weird ever since the picnic."

"I've never known him to keep quiet so long," said Dave.

A waiter walked by, pushing a cart loaded with food. The wild chipmunk's eyes lit up and he leaped…

…smack into the middle of the mashed potatoes! A shower of food flew up, covering the nearby diners.

"For pity's sake," said Dave. "What's gotten into Alvin?"

"That chipmunk just isn't our Alvin," Theodore whispered to Simon.

"I think Alvin traded places with him at the picnic," Simon whispered back. "Let's get to the bottom of this tonight."

When Simon and Theodore questioned the wild chipmunk, they realized Alvin was still in the woods. Then they knew that Grizzly Sam hadn't been fooling when he'd called Dave. Alvin had been captured and needed to be rescued—fast! The Chipmunks had a concert the next afternoon!

The three chipmunks got up at dawn and hiked through the woods to Grizzly Sam's cabin. Theodore set up a huge cage outside the front door and waited there. Alvin's double stood outside the window. Simon climbed onto the roof, took a deep breath, and dropped down the chimney.

Whoosh! Simon landed in a pile of ashes.

"Pfui!" he spat.

From a cage in the room, Alvin spotted his brother and perked right up.

"Shh!" whispered Simon. He opened the cage. Then the two Chipmunks hid behind a pile of firewood.

Clink, clink. Alvin's double, still outside, tapped a stone against the window.

Grizzly Sam awoke with a snort. "Alvin? Hey, you git back in here!"

Sam went running out the front door and right into the waiting cage. Theodore slammed the cage door with a clang.

Overjoyed, the Chipmunks danced around.

"We did it!" yelled Theodore.

"Boy, am I glad to see you guys again," said Alvin. "Maybe fans aren't so bad after all. This nuts-and-berries life is for the birds."

Alvin and his double changed back into their own clothes. Then Simon said to the wild chipmunk, "Thanks for all your help." They all shook hands and the wild chipmunk scampered off happily into the woods.

"Hey, let's move it," said Simon. "We're onstage at the Forum in two hours!"

Soon Alvin, Simon, and Theodore were traveling down the highway on the fastest thing they could find—a tricycle.

"Faster," said Simon. "We'll never make it."

"My legs are getting tired," Alvin complained.

Honking cars backed up behind them for miles, creating a huge traffic jam. A car with a flashing red light and a siren sped toward them.

"Don't look now," said Simon, "but here come the police."

Back at the house, Dave was frantic.

"Don't those guys know they perform in an hour? Maybe I've been too hard on them. I'll give them a two-week vacation if they'll just come back!"

Then Dave found a note by the phone. It said: "Dear Dave, We took Alvin for a little walk. See you at the concert. Signed, Simon and Theodore."

"Are they kidding?" cried Dave, and he rushed to the Forum. When he arrived, it was showtime—and there was no sign of his boys.

Inside the Forum the impatient fans started chanting: "We want the Chipmunks! We want the Chipmunks!"

A police car pulled up outside the Forum. Three Chipmunks jumped out. "Thanks for the lift, Officer. We'll send you free tickets to our next concert," Alvin called.

The Chipmunks raced past Dave, threw on their costumes, and ran onto the stage. A huge round of applause greeted them.

"Alvin, I love you!" someone cried.

"This is the place for me!" said Alvin. And the Chipmunks began to sing.